evolving
tradition

MUSIC AND WORDS FROM THE EVOLVING TRADITION ALBUMS 1 & 2

published by
dave mallinson publications

in association with
mrs casey music

evolving tradition

evolving
tradition

© 1996 Dave Mallinson Publications and Mrs Casey Music
First produced and published in England 1996 by
DAVE MALLINSON PUBLICATIONS
3 East View, Moorside, Cleckheaton, West Yorkshire, England BD19 6LD
Telephone 01274 876388, facsimile 01274 865208, e-mail mally@jorum.demon.co.uk
in association with
MRS CASEY MUSIC
PO Box 296, Aylesbury, Buckinghamshire, England, HP19 3TL
Telephone 01296 394411, facsimile 01296 392300
ISBN 1 899512 35 7
British Library cataloguing in publication data:
A catalogue record for this book is available from the British Library

Text set in Galliard, display titling in Franklin Gothic; music engraved in Petrucci using *Finale;* page layout in *QuarkXPress*
Data capture by Sarah Coxson and David J Taylor
Data manipulation, typesetting and layout by David J Taylor
All photographs and music are copyright their respective owners and used with permission
Album photographs and cover design by Bryan Ledgard, Ledgard Jepson, telephone 01226 766608
Printed by RAP Limited, Rochdale, telephone 01706 44981

contents

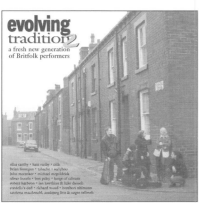

The two albums involved in this project, **evolving tradition** (MCRCD5991 and MCRC5991) and **evolving tradition 2** (MCRCD6991 and MCRC6991), are available from any sensible stockist of traditional music or, of course, from either *Dave Mallinson Publications* or *Mrs Casey Music*, both of whose addresses are shown opposite.

steve heap, mrs casey music

the 1960s saw a great revival of interest in this country's glorious folk music. Clubs and societies flourished and media attention was attracted. By the end of the 1970s, while some clubs were in decline, festivals were increasing in number, supported by those same people who had shown interest in the early years; but who would take over the music?

As though from nowhere in the mid-'80s, the children of those '60s revivalists appeared on the scene, playing and singing to a quality surpassing anything that had gone before. They were a new young generation of musicians and singers with an eye on their roots of music, dance and song and a mind on the future.

We've captured just a few minutes on our albums **evolving tradition** and **evolving tradition 2**. We hope that these pages will encourage yet more to continue the evolution and celebration of the traditional music available in these islands. Get out there and make music.

sarah coxson, mrs casey music

One of the many gratifying factors of working on these two **evolving tradition** compilations has been the sheer volume of great musical talent and potential stars brought to our attention. There have been very many different levels of technical skill but the spirit, understanding and passion of the playing throughout has been heartening.

Hopefully the **evolving tradition** recordings have successfully captured a moment in time, a time when so many young musicians have decided to try their hands at the traditional music of these isles…music which has evolved through the generations and will continue to do so in these upcoming musicians' capable hands.

graham sheffield, barbican centre

the first **evolving tradition** festival in 1995 was a new departure for the Barbican Centre, working with Mrs Casey Music; we were overwhelmed by its success. The Centre was filled over the Easter weekend with innovative and exciting performances of the highest standards, given by a wealth of up-and-coming talent as well as established names in the world of traditional music.

Since 1995, the **evolving tradition** concept has gone from strength to strength, a fact exemplified by the popularity of 1996's festival. The festivals and recordings go hand in hand and the Barbican looks forward to continuing its exciting relationship with Mrs Casey Music in playing a continuing part in the current revival of traditional music from these isles.

Barbican Centre

evolving tradition

Just when some of us had even stopped moaning about the lack of young people playing and singing traditional music and we were tacitly preparing to tick each others' names off in the queue for the funeral parlour, along came a raft of singers and players who fell upon the repertoire with real relish and reminded one that the possibilities are indeed endless.

It's my fervent belief that the only damage to traditional music is done when traditional music is not done at all. It's a music which survives by being passed hand to hand; it does so frequently against the odds. To say that the people involved in **evolving tradition** are technically so much better than we were at the same age states the obvious but misses the point of how good they are on anyone's term. And quite apart from how well they play and sing, the important thing is that in terms of imagination and drive, the best of them give best to no-one. The fact that young people can and do play and sing brilliantly is often seen as extraordinary. Why?…

Martin Carthy

Photograph: Ray Williams

the kings of calicutt

the kings of calicutt 1995

the kings of calicutt, as featured on the first **evolving tradition** album, include young stars *Eliza Carthy* and *Nancy Kerr* alongside melodeon wizard *Saul Rose*. Eliza and Nancy have fast earned themselves a strong reputation for their passionate fiddling and vocal skills.

The band play a selection of English dance tunes and songs and are currently making significant waves on the British folk circuit. The line-up has, since **et1**, expanded to include guitarist *Dan Plews* who appears on the **evolving tradition 2** track contribution and who, in turn, has been replaced by *Maclaine Colston*. **the kings of calicutt** have not recorded as a group to date.

Kit Bailey, Brass Tacks
Orchard House, Gloucester Road, Hartpury
Gloucestershire, England, GL19 3BG
Telephone 01452 700110
Facsimile 01452 700797

contact

the trip to fowey
traditional, arranged carthy, kerr & rose

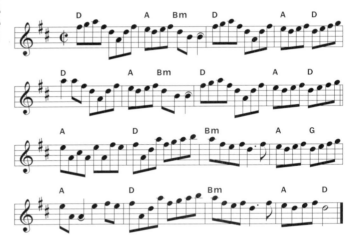

indian queen
traditional, arranged carthy, kerr & rose

evolving tradition

ingrid & allan henderson

Photograph: Mrs A Henderson

ingrid & allan henderson

Scottish multi-instrumentalists **ingrid and allan henderson** appear mostly as a clarsach/fiddle duo playing traditional and original Celtic music.

As well as making music, both are studying Celtic music and history; both players also freelance as keyboard players with various groups. Ingrid is a former BBC Radio 2 *Young Tradition Award* winner. **et1** featured the tune **tom clarke's trip to russia**, which is from their 1994 album *The Perpetual Horseshoe*.

tom clarke's trip to russia
© j sutherland, grian music

Discography
Light of the Mountain (Lochshore LDL1204)
The Perpetual Horseshoe (Lochshore LDL1216)
The Tuning Phrase (Own label)

**Ingrid & Allan Henderson
Ashburn House, Achintore Road
Fort William, Lochaber
Highlands, Scotland, PH33 6RG
Telephone 01397 706000**

contact

Photograph: Derek Botherel

luke daniels trio

luke daniels

luke daniels, 1992 BBC Radio 2 *Young Tradition Award* winner, has constantly developed his music in several directions. A short spell with legendary group *De Dannan* marked not only a commitment to his traditional roots but it also enhanced his reputation on the Irish scene. He's also displayed a progressive fold to his bellows in working with award-winning contemporary jazz group *Scarp*. The British festival circuit has also seen Luke in a duo with guitar wizard *Frank Kilkelly*.

Rarely exposed due to individual commitments, the trio on **evolving tradition 1** featured fiddler **teresa heanue** and guitarist **ian carr**. Luke's solo career was postponed in 1995: he was advised to rest and underwent physiotherapy for paralysis in his right hand due to muscle overuse, but has since used his time wisely, developing skills as a composer, making sporadic solo performances and guesting with the band *Equation*.

teresa heanue is a London fiddle player, of Galway parentage, who is part of a new generation of musicians in Britain making their mark in Irish traditional music. She has won numerous all-Ireland titles and in 1993 appeared on RTE's *The Pure Drop*. She's currently in the band *Sin É*.

teresa heanue

ian carr also features on the tracks on pages 15 and 38 of this book.

Discography
Tarantella (Acoustics ACS023 1994)

Acoustics
PO Box 350, Reading
Berkshire, England, RG6 7DQ
Telephone 0118 926 8615

contact

johnny 'watt' henry's
traditional arranged carr, daniels & heanue

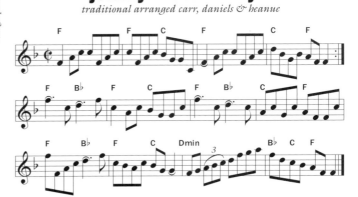

tommy peoples'
traditional arranged carr, daniels & heanue

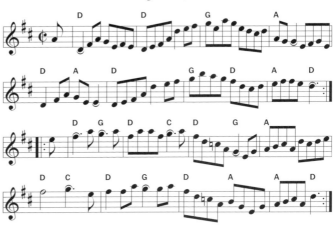

aly bain's
© aly bain

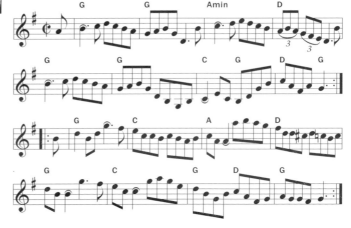

evolving tradition

óige

the flower of magherally
traditional, arranged óige

One pleasant summer's morning, when all the flow'rs were springing out, Nature was adorning and the wee birds sweetly singing out; I met my love near Banbridge town, my charming blue-eyed Sally-o, She's the queen of the County Down, the flow'r of Magherally-o.

Photograph: Danny O'Cathain

óige

óige (pronounced oy-ga) is the Irish word for 'youth' and the Spanish word for 'listen'. The band as was - all from the small town of Dungiven, County Derry - featured *Cara Dillon* (now having left to join *Equation*) on vocals, fiddle and bodhrán, *Murrough O'Cathain* on flutes and whistles, *Ruadhrai O'Cathain* on fiddle and bodhrán and *Paul McLaughlin* on vocals and guitar. The band's roots are in traditional music, played in a unique style using their own arrangements on acoustic instruments. This evocative song, **the flower of magherally**, features Cara's voice accompanied by Paul on guitar from a performance captured on their live album which was recorded in Scotland.

The band's latest album, featuring vocalist *Marranna McCloskey*, is entitled *Bang On* and is due to be released in June '96 by Lochshore Records (LDL1241).

2
With admiration I did gaze upon this blue-eyed maiden,
Adam wasn't half much pleased when he met Eve in Eden;
Her skin was like the lily-white that grows in yonder valley-o,
She's my queen and my heart's delight, she's the flower of Magherally-o.
3
Her yellow hair in ringlets fell and her shoes were Spanish leather,
Her bonnet with blue ribbons strung and her scarlet cap and feathers;
Like Venus bright she did appear, my charming blue-eyed Sally-o,
She's the girl that I love dear, she's the flower of Magherally-o.
4
And I hope the day will surely come when we'll join hands together,
'Tis then I'll bring my darling home in spite of wind and weather;
And let them all say as they will and let them reel and rally-o,
For I shall wed the girl I love, she's the flower of Magherally-o.
Repeat verse one.

Discography
Inspiration (Own label)
Live (Lochshore LDL1225)

John Morgan
Carrick Music Agency
Whin Cottage, Dundas Street, Comrie
Perthshire, Scotland, PH6 2LN
Telephone and facsimile 01764 679465

contact

Photograph: Lee Donane

dan plews & cath james

cath james & dan plews

Fiddle player and BBC Radio 2 *Young Tradition Award* finalist **cath james** and Milton Keynes-based singer, songwriter and guitarist **dan plews** are captured on **evolving tradition 1** playing an uncannily Carthy/Swarbrick-esque piece. Dan's guitar on the recording was in the DADGAD tuning.

The duo, now no longer together, began working together in 1993. Cath has led Sheffield-based ceilidh band *Roger the Badger* for the last six years amongst numerous other musical ventures. Dan has worked with *The Kings of Calicutt* and his band at the time of going to press is called *Dansaul*.

Cath James, 29, Fry's Lane, Yateley Hampshire, England GU17 7TJ
Telephone 01252 872040 or 0114 268 0880
Dan Plews, 192 Church Street, Wolverton, Milton Keynes, Bucks, England NN11 4QQ
Telephone 01908 320803

contact

the flatulent friar of frome
© dan plews

evolving tradition

chris sherburn
& denny bartley

the tamlin's reel
traditional, arranged bartley & sherburn

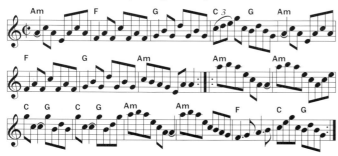

the bucks of oranmore
traditional, arranged bartley & sherburn

bunker hill
traditional, arranged bartley & sherburn

Photograph: Bryan Ledgard

denny bartley & chris sherburn

Although **chris sherburn** has played all kinds of music in the *Green Ginger Band* and the *White Horse Ceilidh Band*, Celtic music is his real love. He broke all the fingers of one hand when he was 20 and was excused physiotherapy on condition he practised hard on his concertina. Since then he has never looked back!

denny bartley has no such history, except that being brought up on the west coast of Ireland is a musical influence in its own right. A cracking singer and guitarist.

Discography
Last Night's Fun (Sound Out Music SOM002)
The Big Noise Upstairs (Sound Out Music SOM001)

**51 Colonel's Walk
Goole, North Humberside
England, DN14 6HJ
Telephone 01405 766352**

contact

evolving tradition

7

nancy kerr & eliza carthy

eliza carthy and **nancy kerr** have been at the forefront of the so-called 'folk brat-pack' scene for almost as long as their soaring twin fiddling and striking harmony vocals hit the stage a few years back. Their youthful ebullience and sparkling talent serves as an inspiration to many other young performers. Their pedigree is, of course, exemplary. Eliza is daughter of revival stars *Martin Carthy* and *Norma Waterson* and Nancy is daughter of piper *Ron Elliott* and singer and instrumentalist *Sandra Kerr*.

"Sometimes it takes the freshness of youth to re-educate us to the glories of our own tradition."
- Colin Irwin, Folk Roots

Discography
Eliza Carthy & Nancy Kerr
(Mrs Casey Records MCR3991)
Shape of Scrape
(Mrs Casey Records.MCR5992)

contact

Kit Bailey, Brass Tacks
Orchard House, Gloucester Road, Hartpury
Gloucestershire, England, GL19 3BG
Telephone 01452 700110
Facsimile 01452 700797

eliza carthy & nancy kerr

the bonny light horseman
traditional, arranged carthy & kerr

Photograph: Bryan Ledgard

Well now, Bo-na-parte he has com-man-ded his troops for to stand, And he's lev-ell'd up his can-non all o-ver the land, Yes he's le-vell'd his can-non the whole vic't'ry to gain, And he's slew my light horse-man re-turn-ing from Spain. Bro-ken-heart-ed I wan-der all for my true lov-er, He's my bon-ny light horse-man in the war has been slain.

2
You should see my light horseman on a cold winter's day,
With his red and rosy cheeks and his curly black hair,
He's a-mounted on horseback, the whole victory to gain,
And he's over the battlefield for honour and fame,
Refrain

3
Oh, you wives, sweethearts and widows, attention I pray,
For my heart it is broken and it's fading away,
I'm a maid so distracted, broken-hearted I wander,
For my bonny light horseman in the war has been slain,
Refrain

4
Now, if I had the wings of an eagle I'd fly,
To my bonny light horseman and there I'd lie by,
And with my little fluttering wings I would build up my nest,
Oh, my bonny light horseman, you're the boy I love best,
Refrain

michael turner's waltz
traditional, arranged carthy & kerr

cythara

p j cunningham's odd dance

© john cunningham

First part harp riff

cythara

Both finalists in BBC Radio 2's *Young Tradition Awards* in 1993, former west country duo *Maclaine Colston* on hammered dulcimer and *Jenny Crook* on Celtic harp played in combination with a technically brilliant and musically fresh sound. They have been featured on several albums and also recorded for television documentaries including David Attenborough's *The Private Life of Plants*. They have appeared on BBC1's *Pebble Mill* and *Summer in the City;* radio performances include *Kaleidoscope* on Radio 4, *Harps in Concert* and *Folk on 2 in Concert* amongst others.

· Maclaine, in 1996, is busy with *The Kings of Calicutt* (see page 30) and his new band *Epona* whilst Jenny has teamed up with fiddle player *Henry Sears* and guitarist and singer *Dominic Harrison.*

"It is the presence of younger musicians of this quality that ensures the continuing vigour of British folk music"

- **Tony Slinger, Venue**

Discography
Cythara (Goldleaf Records/Realwood Music GL1)
Pluckin' Hammered (KRL Lochshore LDL1245)

Jenny Crook
41 Bloomfield Park Road, Timsbury
Bath, Avon, England BA3 1LR
Telephone 01761 470925

Maclaine Colston 0378 452999

contact

Photograph: Dennis Coutts

shetland's young heritage 1995

Renowned Shetland fiddler *Tom Anderson* (1910-1991) not only had the foresight and conviction to collect and archive much of Shetland's folk traditions and music but also had the imagination and determination to pass on what he had learned to a new generation of young Shetland fiddlers. It was one of his greatest hopes and desires that the music of his islands would be kept alive for generations to come. It was on his retirement in the early '70s that Tom found a new career in the teaching of traditional fiddle to hundreds of Shetland children. In 1981 he gathered together some of these pupils to perform at Shetland's local beauty contest and it was from these youngsters - 'Tammy's Peerie Angels' - that this young group started. In 1983, the group was formed into an official society, **shetland's young heritage**, set up to preserve, play and teach the traditional music of Shetland. They have been doing so with great enjoyment and success since that time.

Discography
Visions (Heritage Productions)

Julia Sinclair
12 Montfield
Lerwick, Shetland
Scotland, ZE1 0QA
Telephone 01595 695727

contact

the doon hingin' tie
© iain peterson

tammy anderson
© iain peterson

kate rusby &
kathryn roberts

recruited collier

traditional, arranged roberts & rusby

"What's the mat — ter with you, me lass___ and where's your dash - ing Jim___ mie?" "Them sol - dier boys___ have pick'd him up___ and ta - ken him___ far from me.___ Last pay day he went in - to town___ and them red - coat - ed fel - lows,___ En - tic'd him in___ and made him drunk, And he'd bet - ter gone to the gal - lows."___

Photograph: Bryan Ledgard

kathryn roberts & kate rusby

A pair of fine young instrumentalists and powerful vocalists who have captured the hearts of many musical admirers in the last couple of years. Kate and Kathryn's shared upbringing in Barnsley, South Yorkshire brought them in perfect sympathy with each as musical cohorts and in performance.

Their one and only duo album *Kate Rusby & Kathryn Roberts,* which was ably produced by *John McCusker* (see page 38) and from which this beautiful song is taken, brought them huge critical acclaim. Kate now performs as a solo artist and with super-group *The Poozies.* Kathryn, the first singer to win the BBC Radio 2 *Young Tradition Award* (in 1994), now performs with *Equation.*

2
The very sight of his cockade it sets us all a-crying,
And me, I nearly fainted twice, I thought that I was dying;
My father said he'd pay the smart and he'd run for the golden guinea,
The sergeant swore he kissed the book, so now they've got young Jimmie.

3
When Jimmie talks about the wars it's worse than death to hear him,
I must go out to hide my tears because I cannot bear him;
A brigadier or a grenadier they said they're sure to make him,
So now he jibes and cracks his jokes and bids me not forsake him.

4
As I walked o'er yon stubbled field below where runs a seam,
I think on Jimmie hewing there, but it was all a dream,
He hewed the very coyles* we burn, so when this fire I'm leetin,**
To think the lumps was in his hands, it sets my heart a-beating.

5
So break my heart and then it's o'er, oh break my heart my dearie,
As I lie in this cold, cold bed of a single life I'm weary.
Weary.

* coyles = coals **leetin = lighting

Discography
Kate Rusby & Kathryn Roberts (Pure Records PR001)

evolving
tradition

rajan &
rakhi sood

Photograph: Doc Rowe

rajan & rakhi sood

rajan & rakhi sood are a brother/sister musical team based in Middlesex, playing tabla and sitar respectively. The duo contribute to **evolving tradition 1** an improvised piece, an Indian *raag* based on the *kirvani* scale. Both performers have been actively involved with *Roger Watson's* TAPS (Traditional Arts Projects) activities in south-east England, Rakhi is also a fantastic *Kathak* dancer.

Rakhi is a sitar pupil of Baluji Shivastri.

raag kirvani in tintaal

The 'dots' have not been provided for this **evolving tradition** contribution because that is not really the way to approach Indian music!

In very basic terms, this is how it works: the basic scale, or *raag,* is explored by the tuned instrument for a while, without rhythmic accompaniment and then a phrase or two emerges which becomes the basis for the improvisation. This will recur occasionally during the rest of the piece. The exploratory stage is known as *Alaap.* Often, the tabla player will not know which rhythm the piece will emerge into until it does so.

The *Kirvani* scale is south Indian in origin and is close in identity to the western harmonic minor scale: flat third, flat sixth, but sharp eleventh. If you know the English song *Queen of Hearts,* that fits into this scale. The interesting link is that *Kirvani* is considered a 'romantic' raag.

Tintaal is a sixteen-beat rhythm, consisting of four cycles of four beats, the third cycle starting with a weak beat each time: **1** 2 3 4, **1** 2 3 4, 1 2 3 4, **1** 2 3 4. The tabla player develops complexity and trades rhythmic passages with the sitar, or, for that matter, with the dancer's feet, using a choice of learned patterns within the basic structure. It's never the same twice.

With thanks to Roger Watson

catriona macdonald & ian lowthian

faroe rum
traditional, arranged lowthian & macdonald

andowin ida bow
traditional, arranged lowthian & macdonald

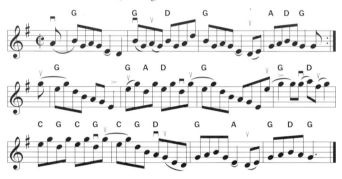

sleep sound ida moarnin'
traditional, arranged lowthian & macdonald

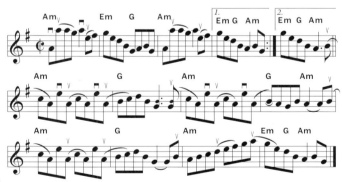

da boanie isle of whalsey
traditional, arranged lowthian & macdonald

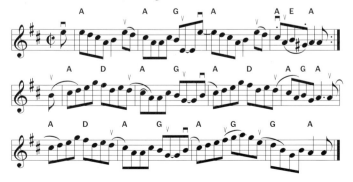

Photograph: Casey Orr

catriona macdonald & ian lowthian

This duo is recognised as one of the finest traditional music products that these islands have seen in a long time. Catriona, winner of the 1991 BBC Radio 2 *Young Tradition Award*, is a Shetland fiddler of the first order. Ian, also a *YTA* finalist, is a superb accordionist from the Scottish borders. The pair are innovative as well as being passionate about their roots. Catriona is one of the late *Tammy Anderson's* star pupils, as well as having been a long time member of *Shetland's Young Heritage* (see page 10).

lasses trust in providence
traditional, arranged lowthian & macdonald

Discography
Opus Blue (Acoustic Radio ARAD103)

Mrs Casey Music
PO Box 296, Aylesbury
Buckinghamshire, England, HP19 3TL
Telephone 01296 394411
Facsimile 01296 392300

contact

the hedgerows

robin hood - the tolling bell
© squeezer records

Spring nine-ty-five and all is not well, The watch-men prowl as the clock strikes twelve, In the dark all-ey-ways on-ly lit by the moon, Where no-bod-y goes and the mon-sters loom, That's where to go to find a way, To see through the mists that hang al-ways, A place where no-bod-y dares to look, The last pa-ges of the old-est book.

the hedgerows

Featuring a progeny of one of England's finest button accordion players *John Kirkpatrick*, *Benji Kirkpatrick* sings and plays guitar and mandolin with this young acoustic outfit from Shropshire. The other half of the duo is *Stephen Bradley* (aka *Bod*) with his ability to produce an awesome range of sounds from the bodhrán. The line-up at the time of this recording featured *Emma Heath* on vocals, *Ben Rodway* on mandolin and recorder and *Spike* on bongos.

The band, who draw on their personal experience of traditions for inspiration, have subsequently gone on to support bands such as *The Oyster Band* and have been seen at *Sidmouth* and *Towersey* festivals amongst others. Their songs are truthful and striking and most of their material is contemporary - but quite obviously based firmly on the tradition.

2
Traps are set, hidden in the grass,
And we walk barefoot on the broken glass,
The mud gets more as the black rain falls,
The leaves turn white as their blood runs cold,
The footsteps we took in the past,
Are catching up on us now, only too fast,
The mistakes we made now can't be ignored,
They've been crashing down, pushing us to the floor.

3
The veins of the earth are running dry,
The sky darkens as time flies by,
The clouds are gathering for the storm,
Moving unheard as they re-form,
The wind gets closer, picking up force,
And we're all set on its course,
The animals flee, the birds fly away,
We think we can conquer if we stay,
It tears through the land, rips us apart,
Leaving nothing alive in its path.

4
We lie, dying under rocks and stones,
The pain grips us through our broken bones,
We try to move but we're paralysed,
And we can't see through our bleeding eyes,
The trees of the woods that used to be,
Are only ashes now in this burnt country,
The sun, now red, sets in a red sky,
The tears of the moon can't be seen as she cries,
The land is black, for all around,
Not a patch of life can be found,
For the mess we made blocked it all from view,
Just another dead world waiting in the queue.

The Quern, Chapel Lawn, Bucknell
Shropshire, England, SY7 0BW
Telephone 01547 530621
or Brass Tacks
Telephone 01452 700110
Facsimile 01452 700797

contact

evolving tradition

simon thoumire & ian carr

the left side jig
© simon thoumire

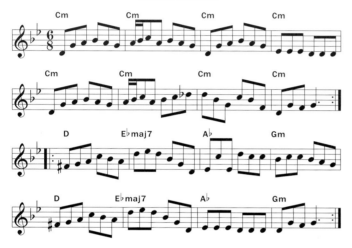

the right side jig
© simon thoumire

simon thoumire & ian carr

Gifted concertina virtuoso **simon thoumire** from Edinburgh plays a pair of self-penned jigs especially recorded for **et1** with supremely talented guitarist **ian carr**. Simon now plays in his own band *The Simon Thoumire Three,* which includes guitarist *Kevin Mackenzie* and *Simon Thorpe* on double bass. He has recorded prolifically since his rise to public attention as the 1989 BBC Radio 2 *Young Tradition Award* winner, bringing to sixteen the number of albums on which he has featured.

Simon is another musician as comfortable with his roots as he is with progressive music making and arguably the first concertina player to be making 'clubbing' records. He has written music for television and been featured in *Aly Bain's* TV programmes *The Shetland Sessions* and *The Transatlantic Sessions.*

Ian is one of the country's most sought-after guitar accompanists. He is a member of the *Kathryn Tickell Trio* and half of a duo with *Karen Tweed.*

Discography
Simon Thoumire & Ian Carr: **HOOTZ!** (CRO225)
Simon Thoumire Three:
Waltzes for Playboys (ARAD102)
Simon Thoumire & Fergus Mackenzie:
Exhibit A (IR31)
Simon Thoumire Three:
March, Strathspey & Surreal (Green Linnet)

**HOOTZ! Productions, 17 Redford Drive
Edinburgh, Scotland, EH13 0BL
Telephone 0131 441 3135
Facsimile 0131 441 3189
E-mail hootz@dial.pipex.com**

contact

evolving
tradition

Photograph: Rosie Maguire

gavin lewery & jock tyldesley

Two of Britain's foremost Cajun musical talents. For many years, **jock tyldesley** has been recognised as the finest fiddle player and **gavin lewery** as the most authentic exponent of accordeon of Louisiana dance-hall sounds in this land. Their kicking contribution to **et1**, the *Canray Fontenot* and *Alphonse Bois Sec* composition **jolie bassette**, (which means a *pretty* and *short woman*) was recorded with Gavin playing his one-row four-stop accordeon tuned in the key of Bb and Jock taking his fiddle down to F-C-F-C from the more normal G-D-A-E.

The pair both stick to authentic '30s and '40s styles of Cajun playing and have fronted hugely successful Cajun bands including *The Flatville Aces, The Bearcat Cajun Playboys, The Bluebird Cajun Band, Zydecomotion* and many more.

The duo will now be concentrating a lot more on their work together, displaying their rare talent, with evocative French vocals and stomping rhythmic playing.

Discography
Flatville Aces:
Crawfishtrombones (Flat Records FLT123)
The Boat Band:
Back Up And Push
Take Me Over The Tide
J C Gallow and The Boat Band:
Fait Pas Ça (Harbourtown)

Becky Morris
Smallworld Music
PO Box 2259, London, England, E17 4RD
Telephone 0181 520 2773
Facsimile 0181 520 5205

contact

evolving tradition

jolie bassette
© ardoin & fontenot

T'as me fait du mal,_____ bas-sette,_____ mais
moi je peux p'us t'ai - mer, Tu
m'as quit-té_____ mi - gnonne,
toi, t'es trop_____ ca - naille._____

2
Ça me fait du mal, 'tit monde,
Moi, je veux plus te revoir,
Ça me fait de la peine, catin,
Toi, t'es trop canaille.
Un jour à venir, mignonne, toi, tu vas pleurer.
3
Mais, moi, je n'en va's mignonne,
Chère jolie bassette,
Tu me fais du mal, catin,
Moi je peux pas t'aimer.

tim van eyken
& kerensa wragg

tralee gaol
traditional, arranged van eyken & wragg

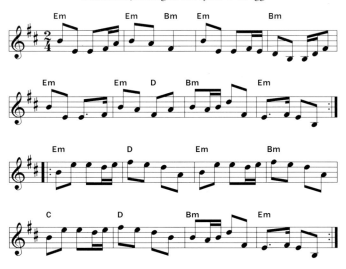

the chanter
traditional, arranged van eyken & wragg

kerensa wragg & tim van eyken

tim van eyken is a *Folk South West* prodigy and **kerensa wragg** a fine talent on hammered dulcimer. The duo met as winners of the *Fylde Folk Festival Young Performers' Competition*. The pair have both been actively involved in various youth movements. They were involved in setting up *Acoustic Youth* and Tim now runs *Shooting Roots,* which aims to help other young folk artists achieve a platform for recognition.

Tim, who has been described as 'frightening' by his tutor *Andy Cutting,* has a colourful and sensitive style. Kerensa is active in *Roger Watson's* TAPS projects.

Tim: Appledore, Old Wells Road, Shepton Mallet, Somerset, England BA4 5XZ
Telephone 01749 343730
Kerensa: 59 Akers Way, Moredon Swindon, Wiltshire, England SN2 2NF
Telephone 01793 613579

contact

carlene anglim & simon haworth

Steeped in a background of Irish traditional music, 1993 BBC Radio 2 *Young Tradition Award* winner **carlene anglim** is master of many Irish fiddle styles and many other traditions from around the world. She is also an all-Ireland fiddle champion. On **evolving tradition 1** she demonstrates those fiddle talents, accompanied by guitarist **simon haworth**.

Simon is a guitarist, cittern player and singer who has worked with the likes of *Alastair Anderson, Clann na Gael* and *Young Tradition* finalist *Amanda Lewis*. He also runs his own radio programme and his current band is *Step Aside* with Amanda and subtle melodeon player *Julian Sutton*.

In the past, the duo have shared stages with the likes of *Liam O'Flynn* and *Arty McGlynn*. Carlene also plays with *Bohinta*. (See opposite)

Carlene Anglim, 2 Kestral Close Hornchurch, Essex, England, RM12 5LS
Telephone 01708 551749
Simon Haworth, 58 Eleventh Avenue, Stobhill, Morpeth, Northumberland, England, NE61 2HT
Telephone 01670 504531

evolving tradition

Photograph: Richard Stewart (Simon)

road to recovery
© liz carroll

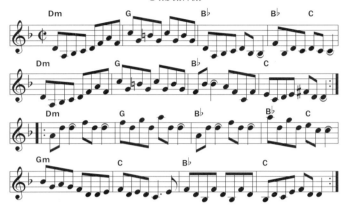

the humours of galway
traditional, arranged anglim & haworth

farewell to the shetland islands
traditional, arranged anglim & haworth

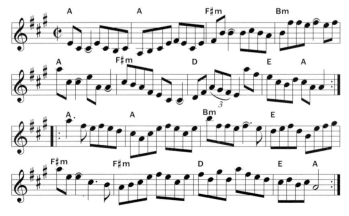

bohinta

lord gresham
© *martin furey*

The bra-zen Lord Gresh-am stares down from the hill, where he sur-veys his lands and men suf-fer his will, For he's a light horse-man and he's ta-ken wing, from fight-ing in bat-tles where man dies for king.

bohinta

Martin Furey (second from left above) and *Áine Furey* (extreme left) of the famous *Furey* family join with percussionist *Greig Stewart* (extreme right) and fiddle player *Carlene Anglim* (front) for one of the many superb songs penned by Martin. The track contributed to **et1** by the quartet, **lord gresham**, captures the more acoustic sound in their repertoire, with the divine voice of Áine taking the lead with Martin.

bohinta, meaning *Banshee,* is now a six-piece 'celtic roots' outfit - the photograph shows bassist *Richard Tobin* at the back and keyboard player *Gil Hunter* in the middle - who are making their own unique contribution to the future of traditional music.

2

He looks for the woman he loved as a girl,
And in that small village her heart thumps with love,
She's found and she's married a young gypsy man,
Who's gentle wild majesty she has let in.

3

Now the brazen Lord Gresham is weary of lies,
As he kneels down before her, that she'd be his bride,
She laughs to the wind, a salt tear to the sea,
Saying, "I will never bow to you and your finery,
"No, I will never bow to you and your finery."

4

"Or will you make me a widow to make me your bride,
"As you made me an orphan when my people died?
"In the fields of starvation where I too could lie,
"But I will never bow to you and your finery."

5

He bursts with an anger, he screams with a pride,
He'll have her as lover and take her as bride,
He's called on his soldiers her gypsy to find,
Saying he's taken his true love for which he must die.

6

The sun bleached the rocks on the cool mountain side,
As they cornered her gypsy 'tween heather and tide,
Lord Gresham has taken his sword in his hand,
With a wave of his cold steel, he's stolen her man.

7

"Oh, darling Lord Gresham, you're brave and you're strong,
"For you've bested my love who could best anyone,
"And yes, I will marry, yes I'll be your bride,
"And I'll go to the altar to stand by your side."

8

She waits at the altar in fear of her life,
For beneath her white petticoat she carries a knife,
Saying, "They'll hang me as murderess, they'll hang me as whore,
"But Lord Gresham will die before this night is o'er."

9

Oh, lifeless Lord Gresham, this widow's no bride,
For you made her an orphan when her people died,
She stands now above you, as proud as can be,
For she will never bow to you and your finery,
No, she will never bow to you and your finery.

Crispin Thomas Management
4 The Retreat, Butterow, Stroud
Gloucestershire, England
Telephone 01453 757376
Facsimile 01453 755024

contact

evolving
tradition

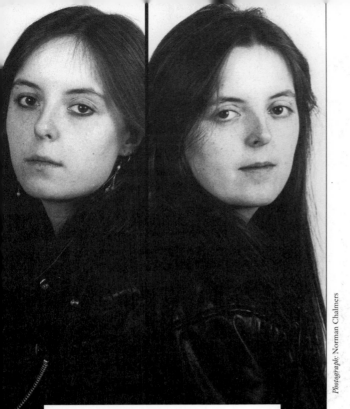

Photograph: Norman Chalmers

jennifer & hazel wrigley

jennifer & hazel wrigley

Originally from Orkney and currently based in Edinburgh, these internationally-acclaimed twins play traditional music and their own compositions with a natural skill, dexterity and grace. With Jennifer, on fiddle, Hazel on guitar or piano, a vital freshness is injected into their arrangements with their jazzy syncopation and lively attack.

Even before turning sixteen, the sisters had a CD and cassette released entitled *Dancing Fingers,* which included a lot of their own material. They have also featured on BBC Scotland and STV.

Their repertoire takes in not only Orcadian traditions, but also those of Ireland, America and the Shetlands. Their contribution to **et1**, taken from their album *The Watch Stone,* is testament to the humour they convey in their playing as well as their technical expertise.

Jennifer and Hazel are now part of *Seelyhoo,* who are featured in this book on page 36.

Discography
Dancing Fingers (Attic Records AT026)
The Watch Stone (Attic Records AT038)
The Scottish Folk Festival '93 (FMS2040)
The Scottish Folk Festival '96 (FMS2065)
Seelyhoo: **The First Caul** (Greentrax TRAX102)

**Stoneyport Agency, 39 Shandon Crescent
Edinburgh, Scotland, EH11 1QF
Telephone 0131 346 8237
Facsimile 0131 313 2083
E-mail jb@folkmus.demon.co.uk**

contact

tom and jerry
traditional, arranged jennifer & hazel wrigley

the
lakeman brothers

the fairfield march
© *seth lakeman*

the rushing reel
© *seth lakeman*

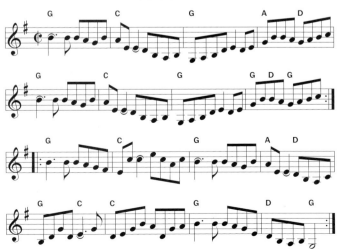

the lakeman brothers

Three Dartmoor-based brothers, *Sean*, *Seth* and *Sam*, on guitar, violin and keyboards respectively. They now make up the core of *Equation*, which also features two wonderful singers in the shapes of *Cara Dillon* and *Kathryn Roberts*.

They have had a strong musical background and education in the folk, classical and jazz fields and their technical virtuosity and sophisticated ear for arrangements belies their tender years.

Discography
3 Piece Suite (Crapstone Records CRM01)

**Crapstone Music Management
The Firs, Crapstone
Yelverton, Devon
England
Telephone 01822 852274**

contact

Photograph: Bryan Ledgard

the chipolata 5

the chipolata 5

the chipolata 5 are a funky five-piece featuring, at their core, street theatre demons *The Chipolatas*. *Sam Thomas* on drums, *Tristan Glover* playing melodeon and *Jasper King* on percussion are quite rightly renowned for their dynamic performance skills; their track on **et1** captures that vibrancy in a musical force to be reckoned with.

The trio are joined by the ace fiddling talents of *Jock Tyldesley* (also featured in this book on page 16) and the bass grooves of *Barnaby Stradling*. The band have whipped up a storm wherever they have played to date and they plan to dedicate far more time to the project, giving an adrenaline spurt to the English ceilidh scene.

the chipolata 5 will be releasing an album in the summer of 1996.

contact

**Chapel House
132 Wincobank Avenue
Wincobank, Sheffield
South Yorkshire, England, S5 6BB
Telephone and facsimile 0114 242 0322**

bransle du chien
© bill martin

bar room brawl
© rob kay

evolving tradition 2

I have never felt comfortable with the term *folk revival* because as far as I'm concerned, the tradition has never stopped. It may seem healthier in Ireland and Scotland, but you can still find traditional music, dance and ceremony in their proper settings all over all of these islands. Those settings have adapted and changed over the years as life has changed and the following pages contain a further album's worth of music-making in an evolving tradition.

No-one who heard **et1** will be surprised at the level of skill and commitment from the singers and musicians on **et2**; likewise, they will be delighted to find that the net has widened to include contributions from Canada, Scandinavia, the U.S.A. and Germany. I repeat: here is another generation of musicians and singers who have been moved by the beauty and passion of traditional music; music which stems from the very stuff of people's lives. Love, death, passion, parting, grief, sorrow and of course, just having a good time.

Norma Waterson

tabache

Photograph: Gordon Hotchkiss

tabache

tabache are a duo comprising fiddle player *Aidan O'Rourke* and flute, tin whistle, fiddle player and singer *Claire Mann*. The pair got together in late 1994 and specialise in traditional Irish and Scottish music. They have completed their debut album with guitarist *Tony McManus* and percussionist *Steve Lawrence* who are both featured on the **et2** track. It is to be released in the summer of 1996 on Klub Records.

The duo have a cabinet stuffed with awards: Aidan has been a *National Fiddle Champion of Scotland* twice; Claire has 3 all-Ireland championship titles on flute and tin whistle.

tabache appears courtesy of *KRL, Glasgow, Scotland*

contact

**Aidan O'Rourke
Burnside, Clachan-Seil, By Oban
Argyll, Scotland, PA34 4TL
Telephone 01852 300554**

dr gilbert's
traditional, arranged tabache

the chicken reel
traditional, arranged tabache

johnny harley's reel
© *liz carroll*

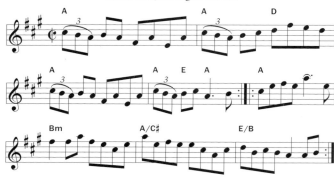

ian lowthian
& luke daniels

luke daniels & ian lowthian

Two of the country's finest exponents of squeezeboxes, **luke daniels** on button accordeon and **ian lowthian** on piano accordion. Both have a thorough understanding of traditional music but feel no formal musical constraints with their innovative outlook and progressive arrangements. Their **et2** track could be described as a 'free folk' piece - dynamic new music making for the late '90s.

ale is dear
traditional, arranged daniels and lowthian

© *1996 Dave Mallinson Publications*
& Mrs Casey Music

Photograph: Tom Howard

eliza carthy

eliza carthy

10,000 miles is from **eliza carthy's** fabulous critically-acclaimed solo album, *Heat, Light & Sound*. It is a superb launching pad for Eliza and indeed many other young musicians.

Vehemently out and proud to be an English folk singer, Eliza has attracted more mainstream attention in the press with her album than most folk musicians have in a life-time.

"The future of British folk is in safe hands."

- Mojo Magazine

Discography
Heat, Light & Sound (Topic TS482)

Kit Bailey, Brass Tacks
Orchard House, Gloucester Road, Hartpury
Gloucestershire, England, GL19 3BG
Telephone 01452 700110
Facsimile 01452 700797

contact

10,000 miles
traditional, arranged carthy

Fare you well,_____ my__ own true love,

fare-well___ for a while,____ I'm go-ing a-way,___

____ but___ I'll be back, if I

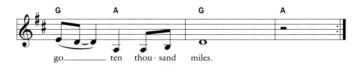

go___ ten thou-sand miles.

2
Ten thousand miles,
It is a long way,
Ten thousand miles or more,
And the rocks may melt,
And the seas may burn,
If I no more return.

3
Oh, don't you see,
Yon lonesome dove,
Sitting on yon ivy tree,
She's making her moan,
For the loss of her own,
As I shall do for mine.

4
Oh, come back,
My own true love,
And stay a while with me,
For if I knew a friend,
All on this earth,
You've been a friend to me.
Repeat verse one

richard wood

trip to the doryman
traditional, arranged wood

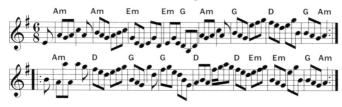

jig
traditional, arranged wood

jig
traditional, arranged wood

two name jig
© *k beaton*

jig
traditional, arranged wood

richard wood

One of the best, if not *the* best, of the young fiddle talents emerging from the Cape Breton region at the moment. **richard wood**, still in his teens, shows in this set of tunes the dancing rhythms and crisp melodies which, whilst clearly springing from a Celtic background, firmly identify themselves as belonging to Nova Scotia.

A vivacious and technically adept player, he made his first album at the tender age of 13! What's more, he's an award-winning step-dancer, winning his first trophies when he was only 8. A major feature of Richard's highly appealing act includes playing the fiddle and step-dancing simultaneously.

Not only does Richard play a lot of traditional material, as the track on **et2** demonstrates, but he also composes in the traditional vein and several of his tunes appear on his albums. Richard is also much in demand as an accompanist - but on the piano. A gifted and inspiring musician.

Discography
Cutting the Bow (own label)
All Fired Up (own label)
The Celtic Touch (Atlantica RW1995)

**Marco Polo, 3, The Lilacs, 50 Elm Grove
Hayling Island, Hampshire, England, PO11 9EF
Telephone 01705 461934
Facsimile 01705 461935
E-mail 100067,2545@compuserve.com**

contact

evolving tradition

catriona macdonald, annbjørg lien & roger tallroth

tallroth, macdonald & lien

Shetland's young fiddling star **catriona macdonald** joins with Norwegian *Hardanger* fiddle ace **annbjørg lien** and Swedish guitarist **roger tallroth** from renowned group *Våsen* for an exciting Shetland-Scandinavian cultural collaboration. There are many links between these traditions and repertoires, which accounts in part for the fluidity and ease of the trio's playing. **istanbul** is a sparkling track co-written by Roger with *Jonas Ohlsson*.

Mrs Casey Music
PO Box 296, Aylesbury
Buckinghamshire, England, HP19 3TL
Telephone 01296 394411
Facsimile 01296 392300

contact

istanbul
© tallroth & ohlsson

evolving tradition

robert harbron

sherele

traditional, arranged robert harbron

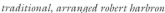

ducks and drakes

© robert harbron

robert harbron

Cumbrian concertina player **robert harbron** has combined a wide variety of influences to produce a unique style of concertina playing. He is a 1992 BBC Radio 2 *Young Tradition Award* finalist and is already a noted composer of tunes. As well as solo work, Robert performs with bodhrán player *Tim Digings* and popular northern ceilidh band, *Jump at the Sun*. Robert plays and dances Rapper with a dance team from his home town of Penrith and runs two groups amidst his final year of A-level studies. One of these groups, *Tich & The Bigots*, recently received a gold medal in the finals of the prestigious *Music in the Community* awards.

Photograph: Ben Deakin

the juggler

© robert harbron

Robert Harbron
Aysgarth, Kirkoswald, Penrith
Cumbria, England
CA10 1EW
Telephone 01768 898533

contact

evolving tradition

the kings of calicutt

the kings of calicutt

The nectar-soaked voice of *Nancy Kerr* leads this raunchy English song supported by a full chorus including *Saul Rose* on melodeon and *Eliza Carthy* playing fiddle. Nancy also plays fiddle. The dance tune that follows covers ground particularly familiar to Saul, from Watford, who is steeped in traditions of playing for Cotswold and north-west morris. Any snooker programme themes heard as a link between song and tune are obviously a figment of everyone's imagination.

the kings of calicutt are joined on the recording by *Maclaine Colston* on hammered dulcimer and *Dan Plews* on guitar. Maclaine is now a member of **the kings**, as is bassist *Barnaby Stradling*.

the buxom lass
traditional, arranged carthy, colston, kerr, plews & rose

Photograph: Sandra Kerr

A labouring lad walk'd out one day and he met with a buxom lass, Belonging to a dairy man, she had a field of grass, It grew between two mountains at the foot of a running spring, She hir'd him out to cut it down while the birds did sweetly sing.

2
He said, "My handsome fair maid, what wages will you give?
"For mowing is hard labour unless your scythe be good."
She says, "If you should please me well, as I am a lady clear
"I will give a crown an acre and plenty of strong beer."

3
He said, "You handsome fair maid, I like your wages well,
"And if that I should mow your grass you'll say it is done well,
"For my scythe is in good order and lately has been ground,
"And so, bonny lass, I'll mow your grass till it's down unto the ground."

4
With courage like a lion he entered in the field,
But before he had mowed one swathe of grass he was obliged to yield,
Before he had mowed one swathe of grass his scythe was bent and broke,
She said, "My handsome fair man, you're tired of your work."

5
She said, "My handsome fair man, you're tired of your work,
"Oh, mowing is hard labour and weakening to the back,
"Yes, mowing is hard labour and it you must forsake,
"But around my little meadow, you may use your fork and rake."

6
He said, "My handsome fair maid, pray do not on me frown,
"For if I stayed the summer long I could not cut it down,
"For it is such a pleasant place and grows such crops of grass,
"For it is well-watered by the spring that makes it grow so fast."

three around three
traditional, arranged carthy, colston, kerr, plews & rose

Kit Bailey, Brass Tacks
Orchard House, Gloucester Road, Hartpury
Gloucestershire, England, GL19 3BG
Telephone 01452 700110
Facsimile 01452 700797

Contact

céile

mullingar races
traditional, arranged céile

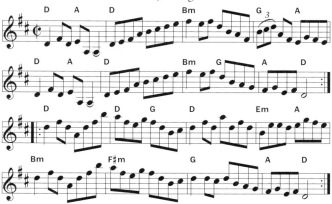

the abbey reel
traditional, arranged céile

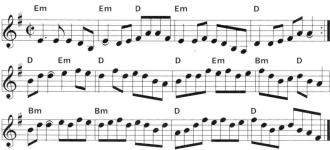

my love is in america
traditional, arranged céile

hanley's tweed
traditional, arranged céile

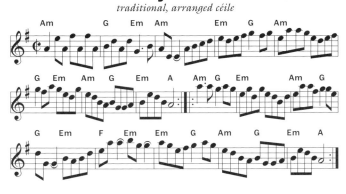

Photograph: Mike Pollard

céile

Manchester-based five-piece **céile** (pronounced kay-ler) play their own arrangements of traditional Irish material as here and also contemporary songs and tunes from their own pens. The band features *Ged Stenson* on flute, fiddle player *Colin Farrell, Nathan Finn* on double bass, *Colin Harries* on guitar and button accordeonist *Eamonn Dinan.*

travers' no. 2
traditional, arranged céile

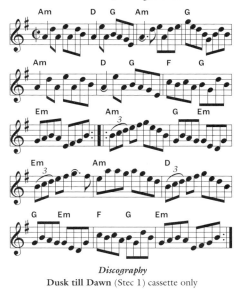

Discography
Dusk till Dawn (Stec 1) cassette only

cordelia's dad

Photograph: Tobey

may blooming field

words traditional, arranged cordelia's dad, tune © eriksen

A wa-ger, a wa-ger and you will go with me, A-way to the May bloom-ing field, A maid-en you will go to the Bloom-field Hill, But a maid-en you ne-ver will re-turn.

2
A wager, a wager and I will go with you,
Away to the May blooming field,
A maiden I will go to the Bloomfield Hill,
And a maiden I will return.

3
So away went this young man, his wager for to win,
Away to the May blooming field,
He sat himself down by the clear flowing stream,
And he fell fast asleep on the bank.

4
Nine times she walked 'round the crown of his head,
And nine times she walked round his feet,
Nine times she kissed his red ruby lips,
As he lay on the bank fast asleep.

5
And the ring that she wore on her little finger,
The same did she place on his own,
That it might be a token of her love to him,
That she had been there and was gone.

6
If I was awake as I was asleep,
This maiden, she never would have fled,
It's her I would have killed, her blood I would have spilled,
And the birds told the story of the dead.

7
Oh, hard-hearted young man, hard-hearted youth,
Your heart's as hard as any stone,
For to think to kill one who has loved you so long,
And will weep o'er the grave you lie in.

"Each verse has variations in pitch, tempo and straightness of rhythm. We do it one way on our record, other ways at other times. Please don't stick to the written music." - Cordelia's Dad

---

cordelia's dad

An American trio featuring *Tim Eriksen*, (voice, guitar, banjo), *Peter Irvine* (voice, drums) plus *Cath Oss* (voice, bass). Operating in two extremely different musical worlds - rock and folk - they find common ground not in a superficial melding, but in stylistic and thematic commonality. **may blooming field**, from their 'acoustic' repertoire, is a modal tune sung with variations not uncommon in rock singing, with both guitar and drum emphasising the tune rather than playing chords and straight rhythm. 1995's album, *Comet*, contained acoustic versions of American songs popular at various times in the country's history plus tracks of original rock music. In 1996, the band gives a glimpse of what they mean by 'rock' with *road kill*, a live album of new and old songs with all the noise and voltage of their 'electric' side. Included below is *The Hookes' Regular Sing*, shape note songs mainly from New England and sung by related group *Northampton Harmony*. All except *Joy Fun Garden* are available through Direct in the UK.

Discography
road kill (Scenescof scof1004) CD only
Comet (Normal/Omnium normal179) CD only
Joy Fun Garden (Steeple Stp001) Cassette only
how can I sleep? (Normal/Omnium OKra33019)
Cordelia's Dad (Normal/Omnium OKra011)
The Hookes' Regular Sing (Hazmat Records has047D)

Contact

PO Box 175
Northampton
MA 01061, USA
E-mail Steeple@world.std.com
http://www.omnium.com/pub/omnium/cdad/

brian finnegan &
austin maguire

headrush 1
© finnegan, maguire & mcilvogue

headrush 2
© mcilvogue

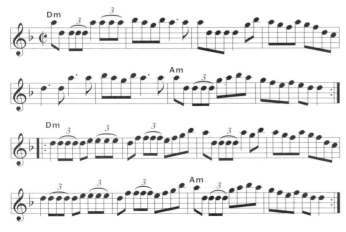

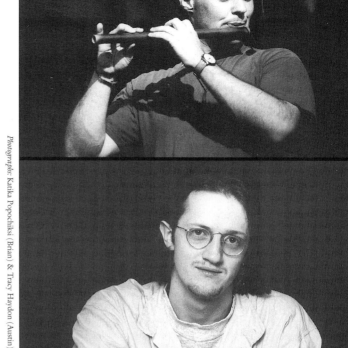

Photographs: Katka Popochiksi (Brian) & Tracy Haydon (Austin)

brian finnegan & austin maguire

Ace flautist and whistle player **brian finnegan** joins together with **austin maguire**, a composer from Fermanagh for a stunning and innovative track. Brian appears as a solo artist and with flute trio *Fluke!* (See page 35). He was formerly in *Upstairs in a Tent* and is now resident in Budapest.

Austin laid the traditional and classical foundations of his musical career at a very early age and recently graduated from University College, Salford, where he studied popular and contemporary music. His work as a soundtrack composer demands extensive research of an unusually diverse range of ethnic musical traditions from all around the world.

headrush was designed to marry the past and the present and thus expose the true beauty of traditional Irish music to a much wider audience. This is the first time Austin and Brian have collaborated on a project of this nature. Hopefully it won't be the last!

"Finnegan really is a thrilling talent, his marvellous technical dexterity, bold musical imagination and urgent tone combining in playing of breathtaking suppleness and delicacy."

Discography
When the Party's Over (Acoustic Radio ARAD101)

evolving tradition

ben paley

ben paley has played fiddle music of the USA, Sweden and Ireland since he was six, has toured widely with his father *Tom Paley* (founder member of the seminal *New Lost City Ramblers*) and now works with accordionist and singer *Bing Lyle*. Their debut album *We are Melting* has received widespread critical acclaim. Ben's collection of Swedish fiddle tunes, *Swedish Fiddle Music: an Anthology* is a standard work in the UK. He has already worked with a wide range of artistes such as the *Saw Doctors*, *The Levellers* and *Herbie Flowers* and others; the discography below is far from complete.

Notation of the tune on **et2**, **frisells storpolska**, or *Frisell's big polska*, can't do it justice. As with much traditional music, dots on their own aren't ideal but written music can help decipher what one is hearing. Chords have not been added: the second fiddle part creates harmony; adding standard guitar chords seems inappropriate.

"Just about the best folk fiddler of his generation."
- **Folk Roots**

Discography
Ben Paley: **Swedish Fiddle Music** (Dragonfly DF002)
Ben Paley & Bing Lyle:
We are melting (Bowsaw BS078)
Tom Paley & Ben Paley:
On a Cold Winter Night (Marimac C9050)
Tom Paley & Barbara Lester with Ben Paley:
Heartease (Just a Person)

Ben Paley
45 Round Hill Crescent
Brighton, Sussex, England
BN2 3FQ
Telephone 01273 626548

contact

ben paley

frisells storpolska
traditional, arranged paley

Photograph: Nick Clyne

evolving tradition

michael mcgoldrick

jenny picking cockles
traditional, arranged mcgoldrick

the earle's chair
traditional, arranged mcgoldrick

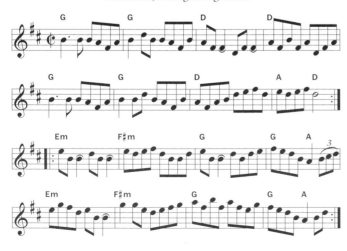

Photograph: Corinne Laffay

michael mcgoldrick

1995 winner of the BBC Radio 2 *Young Tradition Award*, **michael mcgoldrick** is a stunning young player who has a host of accomplished and seminal Irish musicians flocking around him at present. He won the all-Ireland championships on flute and on whistle in 1989 and is a long-time member of Manchester band *Toss the Feathers*. He is now concentrating much more on solo work. He is also one third of flute-toting trio *Fluke!* (see page 33).

His contribution to **et2**, notated here, will feature on his album entitled *Michael McGoldrick* which is due for release in 1996.

Becky Morris, Smallworld Music
PO Box 2259, London
England, E17 4RD
Telephone 0181 520 2773
Facsimile 0181 520 5205

contact

evolving
tradition

Photograph: Simon Saffery

seelyhoo

seelyhoo is an old Scottish word given to the thin membrane sometimes found on a newborn baby's head and is an omen of good luck. **seelyhoo**, the band, with its sheer depth of talent, variety of influences and its creative innovation, is storming the ramparts of the celtic mainstream.

Featuring *Jennifer* and *Hazel Wrigley* (see page 20) amongst the line-up, their debut album *The First Caul*, from which this track comes, is a veritable feast of exciting and confident musical styles. The band also includes *Fiona Mackenzie* on vocals, percussionist *Jim Walker*, *Sandy Brechin* playing accordion and *Aaron Jones* on bass and bouzouki.

Discography
Seelyhoo:
The First Caul (Greentrax recordings TRAX102)
The Scottish Folk Festival '96 (FMS 2065)
Sandy Brechin: **Out of his Box** (BAR6001)
Burach: **The Weird Set** (Trax)
Isabel MacAskill: **Sioda** (SKYE06)
Rod Stewart
and the Glasgow Gaelic Musical Association Choir:
Spanner in the Works
Freeland Barbour & Iain Fraser: **Northlins** (Iona Records)
Wendy Stewart: **About Time** (Greentrax)
Talitha Mackenzie: **Solas** (Riverboat Records)
Ceolbeg: **Unfair Dance** (Greentrax)
Ceolbeg: **5** (Greentrax)
Dancing Fingers (Attic Records AT026)
The Watch Stone (Attic Records AT038)

contact

**Jim Walker
3 Links Gardens, Leith
Edinburgh, Scotland EH6 7JH
Telephone 0131 554 9328
Facsimile 0131 478 0004**

seelyhoo

sean mcguire
© bert murray, arranged seelyhoo

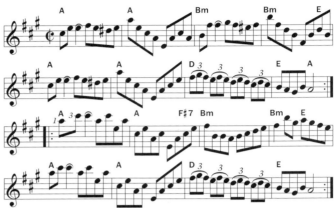

bear island
traditional, arranged seelyhoo

drever's reel
© jennifer wrigley, arranged seelyhoo

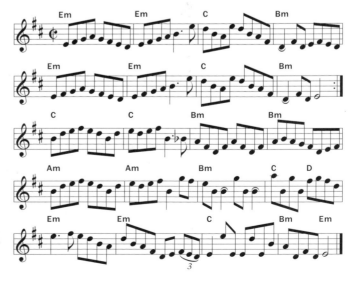

oliver bootle

two ravens
traditional, arranged bootle

As I was walk——ing all a-lone,———

I saw two ra——vens make their—moan,——— And the

one un-to,——— oh, the oth——er say -o,

"Where shall we go and dine to-day—o?

Oh,—where shall we go and dine——to—day?"

2
It's way behind the far end dyke,
It's there I've seen a new-slain knight,
And there's nobody knows that he lies there-o,
But his hawk, his hound and his lady fair-o,
But his hawk, his hound and his lady fair.

3
His hawk is to the hunting gone,
His hound to fetch the wild fowl gone,
And his lady's taken, oh, another mate-o,
So we can have a dinner sweet-o,
So we can have a dinner sweet.

4
You sit on his horse's back,
While I, from his head, oh, his eyes I'll take,
We'll have a lock of his golden hair-o,
To mend our nest when it grows bare-o,
To mend our nest when it grows bare.

5
There's nobody knows for him to mourn,
And there's nobody knows where he is gone,
But his white bones, when they grow bare-o,
Oh, the wind shall blow for ever more-o,
Oh, the wind shall blow forever more.

oliver bootle

oliver bootle is a fiddle player from the Hastings area of east Sussex. He has sung folk songs since an early age and was inspired to play his chosen instrument by *Barry Dransfield,* who taught him to play the fiddle on the lap, a traditional position ideal for self-accompaniment.

Whilst at university in Leeds, Oliver played in many Irish sessions and with numerous bands, including *Slur.* Since then he has played as a solo performer and was a finalist in the 1995 BBC Radio 2 *Young Tradition Awards.* He now works with melodeon player *Ben Dauncey,* also a YTA finalist.

contact

10 Tillingham Avenue
Rye, East Sussex
England
TN31 7BA
Telephone 01797 224875

john mccusker

Photograph: Marc Marnie

john mccusker

Scottish heroes *Battlefield Band's* superb young fiddle player is featured on **et2** in his own right. From his eponymous solo album, John's track here features two of his own tunes, accompanied by guitarist *Ian Carr* and flautist *Iain MacDonald*.

Below is but a brief selection of recordings featuring John, although he has appeared on around forty, including albums by *Teenage Fanclub*, *The Silencers*, *BMX Bandits*, *The Radio Sweethearts* and *Kate Rusby*. John is also fast becoming a respected recording studio producer.

A book of John's tunes is scheduled to be published by *Kinmor Music* late in 1996.

Discography
Solo:
John McCusker (Temple COMD2059/CTP059)
Battlefield Band:
New Spring (Temple COMD2045/CTP045)
Quiet Days (Temple COMD2050/CTP050)
Threads (Temple COMD2061/CTP061)
Parcel O' Rogues:
Parcel O' Rogues (Temple CTP033)
Compilation:
Fiddlers 5 (Temple COMD2044/CTP044)

Robin Morton, Temple Records, Shillinghill Temple, Gorebridge, Scotland, EH23 4SH
Telephone 01875 830328
Facsimile 01875 830392
E-mail 100622.3302@compuserve.com
http://www.rootsworld.com/temple/battlefield.html

st bride's way
© kinmor music 1995

the bouncing czech
© kinmor music 1995

kate rusby

annan waters
traditional, arranged m^{c}cusker & rusby

Oh, Annan Water's wondrous deep and my love Anne is wondrous bonny; I'm loath'd that she should wet her feet because I love her best of any. Go saddle for me the bonny grey mare, go saddle her and make her ready, For I must cross the stream tonight, or nevermore I'll see my lady.

Photograph: Bryan Ledgard

kate rusby

kate rusby, as a solo artiste, really comes into her own. Her warm, mature and distinctive voice and multi-instrumental skills have now been added to the all-women super-group *The Poozies*. On **et2** she sings the beautiful traditional song **annan waters** with stalwart accompaniment from *Alan Reid* on harmony vocals, *Eric Rigler* on uilleann pipes and *John McCusker* on fiddle. John also displays yet another of his talents in his job as producer of the track.

Look out for Kate's solo album, due out in late '96.

2
He's ridden over field and fen, o'er moor and moss and many's a mire,
And the spurs of steel were sore to bite, sparks from the mare's hooves like fire;
Oh, the mare flew over moor and moss and when she reached the Annan Waters,
She couldn't have ridden a furlong more had a thousand whips been laid upon her.
And woe betide you Annan Waters, by night you are a gloomy river,
And over you, I'll build a bridge that never more true love can sever.

3
Oh, boatman, put off your boat, put off your boat for gold and money
For I must cross the stream tonight, or never more I'll see my lady;
Oh, the sides are steep, the waters deep, from bank to brae the water's pouring,
And me bonny grey mare she sweats for fear, she stands to hear the water pouring.

4
Oh, he has tried to swim the stream and he swam on both strong and steady,
But the river was deep and strength did fail and never more he'll see his lady,
Oh woe betide the willow wan and woe betide the bush and briar,
For they broke beneath my true love's hand when strength did fail and limbs did tire.
And woe betide you Annan Waters, by night you are a gloomy river,
And over you, I'll build a bridge that never more true love can sever,
That never more true love can sever,
That never more true love can sever,
That never more true love can sever.

Discography
Kate Rusby & Kathryn Roberts (Pure Records PR001)
Intuition (Various Artists, Fat Cat Records FAT 002)

Steve Rusby
17 Darton Road
Cawthorne, Barnsley
South Yorkshire, England, S75 4HR
Telephone and facsimile 01226 790536

contact

brothers uhlmann

Photograph: Andreas Uhlmann

brothers uhlmann

Johannes and *Andreas Uhlmann* formed their own duo in the autumn of 1993 after having played for many years in their family band, *Haus & Hof Kapelle*. The brothers play what they term as 'new and strange European folk music', a mixture of their own compositions and re-arrangements of traditional tunes. Trained in classical violin and trombone, they also use jazz and folk, a scene in which they were brought up, as major influences on their playing. Johannes plays diatonic accordion and violin and Andreas plays trombone, whistle, shawm and darabuka.

In 1994 the duo won the German folk award *Deutscher Folkförderpreis*. This track is featured on the accompanying album. A third 'brother', *Uli Stornowski,* can be seen in the middle of the photograph above. With Uli, they play as the *Brothers Uhlmann Trio*. With their young cousin *Till Uhlmann* on hurdy-gurdy and fiddler/caller *Matthias Erich Weyrich* they appear as *Tyskarna*.

Discography
Deutscher Folkförderpreis 1994 (MDR Kultur 1994)
Acoustic Power (Rum Records LZ2122)
Tanz & Folkfest Rudolstadt '95 (RU96-1)

contact

**Peter Wilson
Rose Cottage, Kings Head Hill
Bridport, Dorset
England, DT6 3DZ
Telephone and facsimile 01308 425713**

j b w
© *johannes uhlmann*

sweet jenny pearce
© *johannes uhlmann*